MultiSource™

SERIES
EDITORS
Margaret Iveson
Samuel Robinson

EDITORIAL
CONSULTANT
Alan Simpson

LITERATURE
CONSULTANT
Rivka Cranley

TEACHER
CONSULTANTS
Bill Talbot
Karen Brust
Janet Hancock
Wendy Mathieu
Kathy Smith

ANTHOLOGISTS
Sean Armstrong
Monica Kulling
Mary Beth Leatherdale

COVER
ILLUSTRATION:
Music Conductor
by Seashore
by Greg Couch

Imagine POETRY Magazine

Contributors

D1479783

Deborah Samuel
is a Vancouver-born
photographer who works with a
wide range of subjects.

Maria Parker Pascua
is a teacher and writer working to
preserve the culture of her whaling
ancestors.

**Alden
Nowlan**
wrote many collections of
award-winning poetry,
much of it about his native
Nova Scotia.

Compliments of ORGANIZATION for LITERACY in LAMBTON
Take
a
Book!
332-4876

Lisa Bullock
is a student in British Columbia.

**Prentice Hall
Canada**
Scarborough, Ontario
© 1993 Prentice-Hall
Canada Inc.
ALL RIGHTS RESERVED

No part of this book may be
reproduced in any form without permission in
writing from the publisher.
Printed and bound in
Canada.
ISBN 0-13-017963-9

Contents

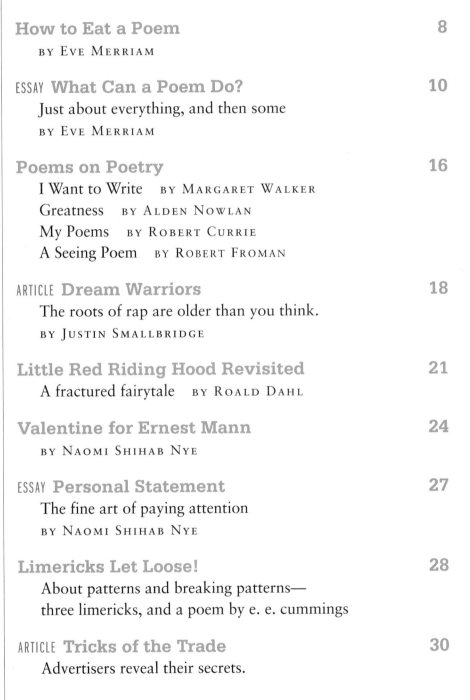

Features

Departments

A poem can be music, flowing over you. Or it can be an explosion, waiting on the page for you to set it off. The rhythms and sounds of poetry are everywhere. A popular rap group creates new poetry from old traditions. An ancient whaling people treat their songs like prized possessions. The words of a Russian poet strike fear in a powerful dictator. Look closely at the world and *imagine poetry.* It may appear unexpectedly all around you.

You are reading this too fast.
Slow down, for this is poetry
and poetry works slowly.
Unless you live with it a while
the spirit will never descend.
It's so easy to quickly cut across the surface
and then claim there was nothing to find.

– Ken Norris

Poetry is a sliver of the moon lost i

– Carl Sandburg

I could no more define poetry than a terrier
can define a rat.   – A. E. Housman

As I am a poet

I express what I believe,

and I fight against whatever I oppose,

in poetry

– June Jordan

the belly of a golden frog.

Cats, Cats, and More Cats

A popular musical introduces millions of people to the poetry of T. S. Eliot.

You now have learned enough to see
That Cats are much like you and me
And other people whom we find
Possessed of various types of mind.
For some are sane and some are mad
And some are good and some are bad
And some are better, some are worse—
But all may be described in verse.

excerpt from "The Ad-dressing of Cats"
T. S. ELIOT *(1888–1965)*

Fanciful cat characters cavort in a giant garbage dump in this scene from the musical *Cats*.

The lines above are from T. S. Eliot's *Old Possum's Book of Practical Cats,* published in 1940. These humorous poems were originally written for Eliot's friends and only later collected and published. Much later still—41 years later, as a matter of fact—they were turned into one of the most successful musicals in the history of theatre: *Cats*. In this show, where actors take the parts of Eliot's odd assortment of cat characters, the fact "That Cats are much like you and me" has entertained millions of people.

It was composer Andrew Lloyd Webber who thought of bringing Eliot's cats to life in a musical. Some of Lloyd Webber's songs are actually Eliot's cat poems set to music, and others are based on unpublished material given to the composer by Eliot's widow. Lloyd Webber described the process of bringing *Cats* to the stage as "a nightmare." After all, who would invest in a play based on children's verses written by a Nobel Prize winner known for his very serious and difficult poetry? Once people heard Lloyd Webber's songs presented at an

arts festival, however, backers were found, and *Cats* headed for the London stage.

On stage, the *Cats* set looks like a huge garbage dump with giant pieces of trash—used toothpaste tubes and broken dishes. Cat characters, including Grizabella the Glamour Cat and Rum Tum Tugger the Curious Cat, frolic in the dump and wander into the audience, getting "oohs" and "ahs" from theatregoers. Spectacular costumes and wonderful songs, such as "Memory," complete the world of *Cats*, a world that won't be forgotten by those who have shared it.

A Different Kind of Athlete

In Japan, writing poetry is both a game and a pleasurable pastime.

Imagine that you and your teammates have been training for months to prepare for a big competition. When you arrive at the site of the match, you walk to the banner-festooned playing area. The other team approaches, and the judges tell you to begin. Then, instead of using a racquet or a bat and a ball, you pull out a pen and writing paper! You are competing with words—in a poetry-writing contest! Such contests have been held for thousands of years in Japan, where poetry writing still is often a group activity.

Centuries ago two forms of poetry were popular in Japan: tanka and renga. Eighth-century tanka poems had 31 syllables arranged in units of 5, 7, 5, 7, and 7 syllables per line. The renga poem, popular in the tenth century, also had 31 syllables, broken into two parts of 17 syllables and 14 syllables. The renga were usually written by two or more people, and renga writing was a popular team sport.

From this tradition evolved the haiku, today the most familiar kind of Japanese poem. Haiku started out as the first part of a renga poem. Eventually the 5-7-5 pattern came to be seen

A Japanese silk painting of the late eighteenth century

as complete in itself. It was the seventeenth-century poet Matsuo Bashō who turned haiku into a refined art, expressing mood and suggesting deeper meaning through concrete images.

> *The lightning flashes!*
> *And slashing through the darkness,*
> *A night-heron's screech.*
> *Matsuo Bashō*

In Japan today, writing haiku is more widespread than ever before. Although group composition is still popular, many Japanese write haiku for their own pleasure. Friends often compose haiku for each other instead of sending greeting cards to celebrate special occasions. Some Japanese families still play a parlor game in which participants draw a line of haiku out of a box and then must provide the rest of the poem from memory.

Haiku has become increasingly popular in English-speaking countries as well. Japanese and English are so different, however, that the seventeen-syllable count does not transfer easily into English. Nevertheless, the spirit of haiku, with its long and respected history, remains the essence of the art.

> *Around the eyes*
> *of the old fisherman*
> *permanent ripples*
> *George Swede*

How to eat

Don't be polite.

Bite in.

Pick it up with your fingers and lick the juice
that may run down your chin.

It is ready and ripe now, whenever you are.

You do not need a knife or fork or spoon

or plate or napkin or tablecloth.

For there is no core

or stem

or rind

or pit

or seed

or skin

to throw away.

by Eve Merriam

poem

ILLUSTRATIONS BY HENRIK DRESCHER

What can a poem do?

By Eve Merriam

How is a poem different from other kinds of writing?

There is no rhyme for *silver*, but a poem can do just about anything else you want it to. It can be solemn or bouncy, gay or sad—as you yourself change your own moods. A poem, in fact, is very much like you, and that is quite natural since there is a rhythm in your own body: in your pulse, in your

HEARTBEAT,

in the way you breathe, laugh, or cry; in the very way you speak. When you run or tap your feet— even when you sit still and dance only with your feelings—there is the rhythm of a poem. Many kinds of rhythms surround us every day of our lives, although we go on our way unaware of them until a poem comes along to bring the hidden *music* out into the open. There is the majestic rhythm of the changing seasons. The daily journey of the daylight and darkness. The man-made rhythms of **motorS.** The tides; the cycle of a seed growing; the great human experience of life, death, and new generations arising.

It is this built-in rhythm or meter, as it is called when it is very measured, that sets poetry apart from prose. A poem has its own portable *music,* like a transistor radio you can carry with you. Just turn it on, tune in, and listen to the music flow: A poem can give you

HIGH TONES, low tones,

f a s t   t o n e s,
slow tones.

How does it create these effects? In addition to rhythm or meter, very often, through rhyme endings. **A rhyme is a chime that rings in time —** like the little typewriter **bell** that **PINGS** out at the end of each row. It can be serious, like rhyming *breath* with *death;* it can be joyful, like matching *spring, wing,* and *sing;* it can also be funny. Thomas Bailey Aldrich, in *The Story Of A Bad Boy,* claimed that his favorite rhyming poem was **Root beer/Sold here.** One of the shortest rhymes in the world is one you probably see every day at traffic intersections:

Go/Slow.

Not all poems have rhyme; blank verse and free verse do not. But a rhyme at the end of a line is like a bow *tying up a package.* It keeps everything neat and tidy and at the same time gives it a festive air.

Another way that poetry expresses itself in musical terms is through alliteration. When the same consonant or vowel sound reappears, that is *alliteration*. It can be lean, long, and lovely; sweet, snappy, spicy; bold, brave. Or it can show up in the middle of a word, or near the end; and sometimes you have to hunt to find it,

far off in a garden of oranges.

But the musical effect is there. When you read a poem, you can go treasure-seeking and look for alliteration letters all along the lines.

Still a third way that poetry's built-in music makes itself heard is through the use of repetition— of words, or entire phrases. They are used over and over (and sometimes over and over and over!) like a melody that returns so that you can recognize it as a familiar friend. The *repetition* may serve to lull you to rest: "hushaby, hushaby, sleep, my baby, sleep." Or it can startle you awake:

"clang, clang, clang
went the cymbal;
bang, bang, bang
went the drums."

You can make whatever kind of music you like with a poem. You can also paint pictures. In a poem, the pictures are called word-images. All of us, every day, use word-images when we talk. We say "it's hot as blazes," "she's slow as molasses," "he's a poke or a stick." We say "my heart was in my mouth" or "I felt all goose-flesh." Some of these word-images have become so worn through usage that we call them clichés. A poem tries to create new word-pictures. Instead of saying hot as blazes, cold as ice, or slow as molasses, a poem seeks out new images for hot and cold and slow.

As you read more poems, and perhaps write some yourself, you will find that some word-pictures, or images, paint things exactly the way they look, and some paint them in terms of something quite the opposite—somewhat like the Roman god Janus, whose name we associate with the first month of the year, and who looked back to the old and forward to the new at the same time. An image in a poem may suit what you are describing so that it feels at home and fits like the old comfortable hat on your head; more often, it may seem strange and unexpected at first, as when the wind suddenly snatches the hat off your head.

You can make music with a poem. You can paint pictures. You can also be a sculptor and carve words into all kinds of shapes. You can make the words in a poem sputter like a fountain, as "the musty fust of a dusty road." You can turn words into tongue-twisters. You can play a game of tag with the words in a poem, use rhymes like a **ball** to
toss
back
and **forth.**
In fact, all kinds of games are possible.

A poem makes you aware of language so that even in prose you can enjoy using words more because you know what tricks they can do and what they can *not* do. Also, because a poem is condensed and makes every word count—like a telegram instead of a longer message—it can help you do setting-up exercises to stretch all five of your senses. When you read a poem, you also savor the texture of the words. You should be able to see, smell, hear, touch, and even taste in a richer, deeper way.

You can write a poem or read a poem about many things. About everything in the world, in fact. It can express your mood or take you out

WORD TALK **Poetry** is written language that is concentrated and imaginative, chosen and arranged for impact through meaning, sound, and visual layout. The words *poetry* and *poem* come from the Greek word *poiein*, meaning to create. In the past, poetry always had meter. Today, some free verse seems very close to speech.

of it. For, although it may seem surprising at first, even if you feel sad or lonely, when you read a poem that speaks of loneliness or sadness, you feel that emotion more intensely, but you also feel happier for sharing the poem's experience and for knowing that you are not isolated in your mood. In a way, it is like the relief of a rainstorm after sullen, glowering clouds; and after the rainstorm, a clearing of the sky.

You may not "get" all of a poem the first time you read it, because the words and the built-in music are so concentrated. Don't let it worry you; just go on to the end and then go back and read it again. You will find that the meaning begins to shine through. For a poem, with its rhythmic effects and use of word-pictures, has more than one level to explore. It becomes like a stone that you skim onto a lake; the ripples widen. New meanings unfold, and you have the pleasure of discovering more and more each time.

To come back to our original question, what can a poem do? Just about everything—even though there is no rhyme for silver. (Or orange. Any others?)

EVE MERRIAM *(1916–1992) worked as a poet, biographer, radio scriptwriter, fashion magazine editor, and teacher. Her poetry has won many honours and awards.*

EXPRESS
YOURSELF

Why do people write and read poems? What can a poem do that prose cannot do?

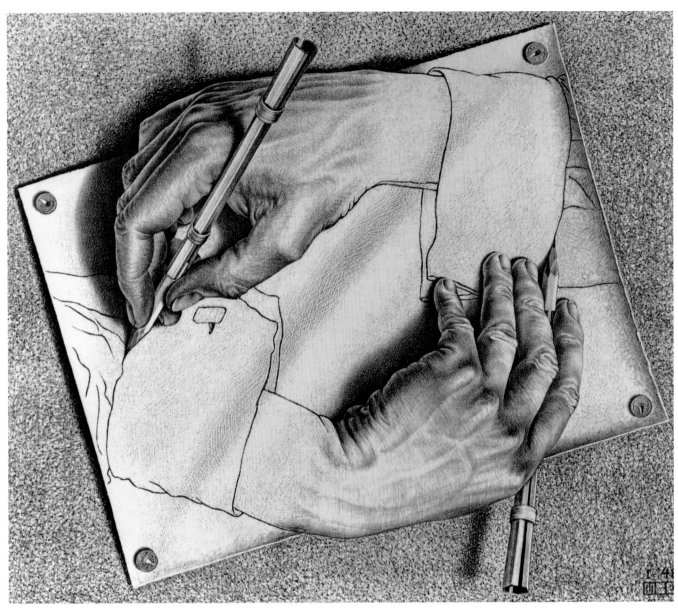

Why do you think poets write about the process of writing?

poems on

I Want to Write

I want to write
I want to write the songs of my people.
I want to hear them singing melodies in the dark.
I want to catch the last floating strains from their sob-torn throats.
I want to frame their dreams into words; their souls into notes.
I want to catch their sunshine laughter in a bowl;
fling dark hands to a darker sky
and fill them full of stars
then crush and mix such lights till they become
a mirrored pool of brilliance in the dawn.

MARGARET WALKER

MARGARET WALKER *was born in Alabama in 1915. She has taught for nearly forty years, most recently as a professor of English. Her first poem, "For My People," is a literary anthem of the Black community.*

Greatness

I would be the greatest poet the world has ever known
if only I could make you see
here on the page
sunlight
a sparrow
three kernels of popcorn
spilled on the snow.

ALDEN NOWLAN

ALDEN NOWLAN *(1933–1983), a Nova Scotia editor and writer, won the Governor General's Award in 1967 for a book of his poetry.*

My Poems

My poems
are slim bombs
craving explosion.
Their fuses lie
dark on the page
awaiting your arrival with a light.

ROBERT CURRIE

ROBERT CURRIE *was born in 1937. Once publisher of a journal of writing, he is now a poet and an English teacher in Saskatchewan.*

A Seeing Poem

ROBERT FROMAN

A SEEING POEM HAPPENS WHEN WORDS TAKE A SHAPE THAT HELPS THEM TO TURN ON A LIGHT IN SOMEONE'S MIND

poetry

ROBERT FROMAN *was born in 1917 in Montana. His books and poems indicate his special interest in math and science.*

Dream Warrior

Canada's hot rap group spins some old themes into an altogether new kind of music. **By Justin Smallbridge**

Music and poetry are closely linked art forms, but exactly what do rap music and poetry have in common?

King Lou and Capital Q don't fit the image most people have of rap stars. They don't wear black clothing plastered with Los Angeles Raiders symbols. The fat gold chains sported by a large segment of the rap community are absent. Neither one wears $200 sneakers. (Their only theatrical prop, other than their names, is Lou's four-foot staff made of a petrified sugar-cane stalk, which has become their talisman on stage.) There is very little in their music, their lyrics, or their personalities that comfortably fits into any popular definition of rap, except that the Dream Warriors, after only one album, have become the country's most interesting and most inventive hip-hop artists.

Rap seems new and unfamiliar, but its roots are deep. The practice of serving up observation, commentary, and insult in rhyme runs like a main-circuit cable through African-American and African-Caribbean oral culture. Anyone who's heard even part of Jesse Jackson's speeches will recognize the cadences and constructions of rap.

One of the earliest forms of rap can be traced back to the turn of the century. In a game called

King Lou and Capital Q in performance, with the four-foot sugar-cane staff that has become their talisman.

"playing the dozens," young men would taunt each other, attacking one another on the basis of poverty, appearance, housing, or parentage. Each player tried to cap the preceding rhyming insult until he couldn't think of an insult or figure out a way to make it rhyme. Such contests usually lasted for about twelve sets of rhymes, hence the term "dozens."

In the Caribbean, the lyrics of calypso songs were composed on the spot during a performance,

and they usually made pointed, funny observations about the politics of the day. In Jamaica, the same tradition turned up as "toasting." Dance hall DJs would play the "dub" or instrumental sides of current singles and offer rhymes—everything from boast-

ing about their own magnificence to social commentary to urging the crowd to dance—at the same rhythm and pace as the accompanying record.

All three strains connected in North America in the late 1960s and early 1970s when millions of Caribbean immigrants moved north, many of them settling in the predominantly Black neighbourhoods of New York City. Playing the dozens was already part of growing up for African-Americans in North American cities, so connecting it with the rhyming oral culture of the West Indies was an obvious step. Jamaican toasting helped turn the whole thing into entertainment. The only difference in the early days of rap was that the backing music came from the instrumental B-sides of funk and soul records instead of reggae singles. And rap—also known as hip-hop—was created.

Almost every rap song is constructed the same way. The necessary musical elements are lifted from existing records by means of digital sampling, then layered on top of each other and mashed together into a sonic collage. By fitting together tiny pieces of other people's music and noise—most of them lasting only seconds—rap artists are able to create something entirely new.

"Whatever idea you've got in your head, the music just goes to

that," Capital Q says of the backing he puts together for Lou's lyrics. "You try to make it fit, with a loud sound or a flowing tempo. It was hard when we first got into the studio, saying, 'I feel I want this in there. Can you get this sound?' Then, we started being able to pick out the sounds we wanted." The Dream Warriors' choice of sounds are every bit as clever and unexpected as their lyrics.

"People condemn sampling," Capital Q says. "But I want to see them sample and create a song if they think it's so simple and such a foolish thing to do. They call it stealing, but it's just another means of creation in music. It's like anything else: using a piece of the old to create the new."

JUSTIN SMALLBRIDGE *is a freelance writer and entertainment reporter for CBC. Born in 1960, he began his journalism career in high school.*

little red riding hood
REVISITED

Why might an author or poet want to rewrite a familiar story? What can they gain from changing a tale that their audience knows well?

"Little Red Riding Hood" is the story of a young girl who travels through the woods to visit her grandmother. She is warned by her mother to stay on the path, but a wolf she meets along the way convinces her to pick flowers instead. In the meantime, the wolf rushes ahead to Grandmother's house, eats Grandmother, and then dresses in her bed clothes. When Red Riding Hood shows up, the wolf eats her too.

At least that was the ending when the tale was published as "Le Petit Chaperon Rouge" in 1697 by Charles Perrault. The Grimm brothers, however, published a version in 1812 in which Rotkäppchen (Little Red Cap) meets with a happier ending: a woodsman arrives to save the day.

On the next page is a present-day interpretation of the fairy tale by the popular author Roald Dahl. Look how the story has changed over three hundred years.

Once upon a time Little Red Riding Hood went through the woods to visit

GRANDMA'S

Little Red Riding Hood and the Wolf

As soon as Wolf began to feel
That he would like a decent meal,
He went and knocked on Grandma's door.
When Grandma opened it, she saw
The sharp white teeth, the horrid grin,
And Wolfie said, "May I come in?"
Poor Grandmamma was terrified,
"He's going to eat me up!" she cried.
And she was absolutely right.
He ate her up in one big bite.
But Grandmamma was small and tough,
And Wolfie wailed, "That's not enough!
I haven't yet begun to feel
That I have had a decent meal!"
He ran around the kitchen yelping,
"I've *got* to have a second helping!"
Then added with a frightful leer,
"I'm therefore going to wait right here
Till Little Miss Red Riding Hood
Comes home from walking in the wood."
He quickly put on Grandma's clothes,

her sick grandmother who lived all alone.

(Of course he hadn't eaten those).
He dressed himself in coat and hat.
He put on shoes and after that
He even brushed and curled his hair,
Then sat himself in Grandma's chair.
In came the little girl in red.
She stopped. She stared. And then she said,

"What great big ears you have, Grandma."
"All the better to hear you with," the Wolf replied.
"What great big eyes you have, Grandma,"
said Little Red Riding Hood.
"All the better to see you with," the Wolf replied.

He sat there watching her and smiled.
He thought, "I'm going to eat this child.
Compared with her old Grandmamma
She's going to taste like caviar."

Then Little Red Riding Hood said, *"But Grandma,*
what a lovely great big furry coat you have on."

"That's wrong!" cried Wolf. "Have you forgot
To tell me what BIG TEETH I've got?
Ah well, no matter what you say,
I'm going to eat you anyway."
The small girl smiles. One eyelid flickers.
She whips a pistol from her knickers.
She aims it at the creature's head
And *bang bang bang,* she shoots him dead.
A few weeks later, in the wood,
I came across Miss Riding Hood.
But what a change! No cloak of red,
No silly hood upon her head.
She said, "Hello, and do please note
My lovely furry wolfskin coat."

ROALD DAHL

ROALD DAHL *(1916–1990) was a British writer of fantastical stories for readers of all ages. He may be best known among younger audiences for his classic tale* Charlie and the Chocolate Factory.

She had not gone far before she met

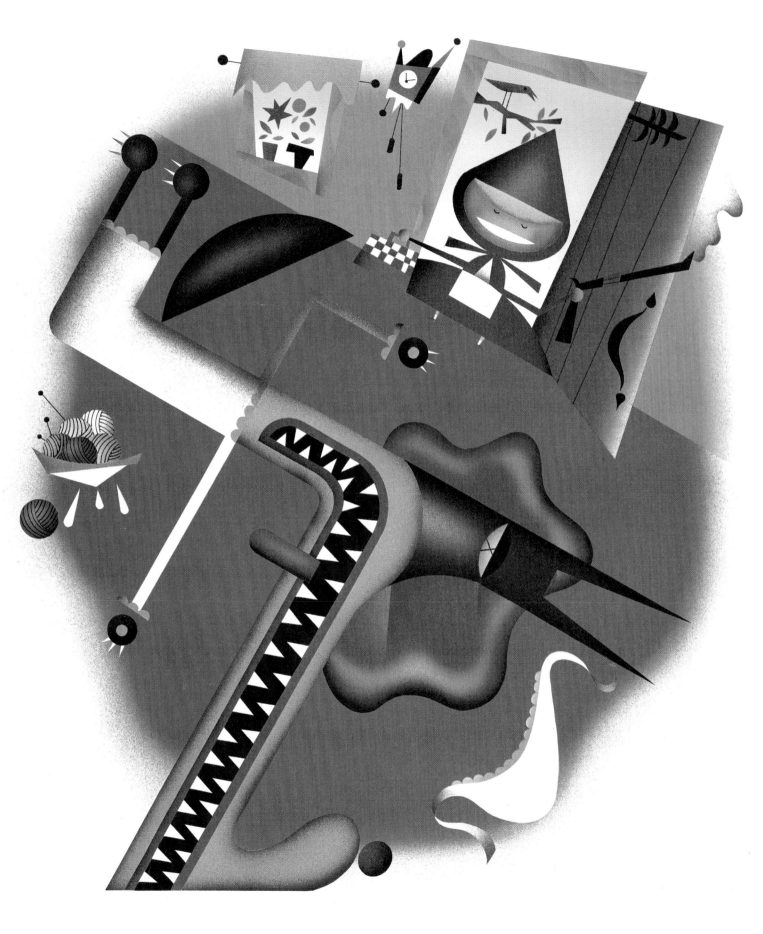

a hungry wolf, who eyed her basket of goodies and said ...

How can a love poem hide in the eyes of a skunk? In what other kinds of places might poems be hiding?

Valentine for Ernest Mann

You can't order a poem like you order a taco.
Walk up to the counter, say, "I'll take two"
and expect it to be handed back to you
on a shiny plate.

Still, I like your spirit.
Anyone who says, "Here's my address,
write me a poem," deserves something in reply.
So I'll tell you a secret instead:
poems hide. In the bottoms of our shoes,
they are sleeping. They are the shadows
drifting across our ceilings the moment
before we wake up. What we have to do
is live in a way that lets us find them.

Once I knew a man who gave his wife
two skunks for a valentine.
He couldn't understand why she was crying.
"I thought they had such beautiful eyes."
And he was serious. He was a serious man
who lived in a serious way. Nothing was ugly
just because the world said so. He really
liked those skunks. So, he re-invented them
as valentines and they became beautiful.
At least, to him. And the poems that had been
            hiding
in the eyes of skunks for centuries
crawled out and curled up at his feet.

Maybe if we re-invent whatever our lives give us,
we find poems. Check your garage, the odd sock
in your drawer, the person you almost like, but
            not quite.

And let me know.

NAOMI SHIHAB NYE

me what's real,

*T*his whimsical portrait by Ivan Chermayeff is made of stamps, packaging materials, and torn envelopes.

*A*rtists and poets have a flair for re-invention. For this two-story-high sculpture, artist Patricia Rennick found her inspiration in an obsolete Volkswagen bug, using it to form the body of a dinosaur.

What

can

you

see

in

a

hunk

of

scrap

metal?

what I see or wh

*D*eborah Butterfield used pieces of scrap metal to create this larger-than-life sculpture of a horse, titled "Joseph." By combining the familiar with the unfamiliar, Butterfield makes people see the world in new ways.

at I feel?"

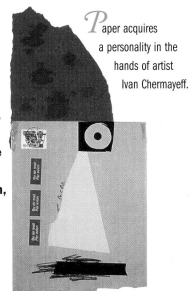

*P*aper acquires a personality in the hands of artist Ivan Chermayeff.

For me poetry has always been a way of paying attention to the world. We hear so many voices every day, swirling around us, and a poem makes us slow down and listen carefully to a few things we have really heard, deep inside. For me poems usually begin with "true things"—people, experiences, quotes—but quickly ride off into that other territory of imagination, which lives alongside us as much as we will allow in a world that likes to pay too much attention to "facts" sometimes. I have always had a slight difficulty distinguishing where the "true" part ends and the "made-up" part begins, because I think of dreaming and imagining as being another kind of *true.* Once I made up a song that ends, "You tell me what's real, what I see or what I feel?", and I think that corresponds to the poems we make out of our lives. Sometimes there's no one to listen to what you really might like to say at a certain moment. The paper will always listen. Also, the more you write, the paper will begin to speak back and allow you to discover new parts of your own life and other lives and feel how things connect. Poets are explorers, pilgrims. Most of the poets I know are not in the least bit frilly. Poets are also regular people who live down the block and do simple things like wash clothes and stir soup. Sometimes students ask, "Are you famous?", as if fame is what would make a poet happy. I prefer the idea of being invisible, traveling through the world lightly, seeing and remembering as much as I can. NAOMI SHIHAB NYE

NAOMI SHIHAB NYE *is a Palestinian American born in 1952 in Missouri. She started writing poetry when she was six years old and published her first poem a year later. She has spent eighteen years visiting schools of all levels to teach writing.*

Limericks

What does a pattern add to a poem?

Patterns in Poetry

Many poems follow traditional patterns that make them easy to read and give them the feeling of a song. The words of a limerick form a rhythmic pattern: the first two lines have the same rhythm, the second two lines have another rhythm, and the fifth line has the rhythm of the first line. The repeating rhythm of syllables within a line is called the *metre*.

Another pattern lies in the way the words of a poem rhyme, called a *rhyme scheme*.

The many different combinations and patterns of *metre* and *rhyme scheme* create unusual and interesting effects.

Breaking the Rules

Sometimes poets work within a particular form or pattern, and then suddenly break the pattern, to bring your attention to something in the poem, such as a joke or a pun.

I sat next the Duchess at tea. ●

It was just as I feared it would be: ●

Her rumblings abdominal ●

Were simply abominable, ●

And everyone thought it was me. ●

A tutor who tooted the flute ●

Tried to tutor two tooters to toot. ●

Said the two to the tutor, ●

"Is it harder to toot or ●

To tutor two tooters to toot?" ●

...let

Breaking the Rules:

l(a

l(a

le

af

fa

ll

s)

one

l

iness

e. e. cummings

e. e. cummings *(1894–1962)*
was born Edward Estlin Cummings
in Boston. In addition to poetry, he
also wrote novels and children's
stories.

A decrepit old gas man named Peter,

While hunting around for the meter,

Touched a leak with his light.

He arose out of sight,

And, as anyone can see by reading this, he

also destroyed the meter.

Anonymous Limericks

Lash Very Lush

Wild Thin.

sensit

avis

a ferocies

tor

The

ROP DEAD N

Spre

Dirty...

Dingy...

Dazzlin

TRICKS OF THE TRADE

Advertisers borrow tricks of the language trade from those other image makers—poets.

How do advertisers engage your attention and get you to remember their products?

Advertising jingles, slogans, scripts, and descriptions—called advertising copy in the ad world—have power, sometimes more power than you might like. They enter your head uninvited and make themselves at home, while you struggle to remember the names of the world's longest rivers or a friend's telephone number. If you watch ten minutes of TV commercials and spend an hour studying French, why is it easier to remember the advertising jingles than the French vocabulary?

Ad copy writers grab our attention with the same tricks that poets have always relied upon. Rhyme. Rhythm. Repetition. Surprises. Puns. Humour. They break grammatical rules, they make up words. And they make us believe they're having fun doing it.

"Whose news do most choose?" asks *MacLean's* maga- zine. "The Bread Spread," chant the mayonnaise people. "Dirty . . . Dingy . . . Dazzling" proclaim the makers of Tide. "Very Lush, Very Lavish, Very Factor" boasts a cosmetics company, counting on name recognition. Revlon's writers get funny with: "Drop Dead Nails" and "Lash chance for sensitive eyes." "A Clearly Grate Italian," puns TreStelle's Parmesan cheese ad. "Wild Thin . . . a ferocious flavour expe- rience," says Diet Orange Crush.

Ad copy writers use words that are juicy and slurpy. Words you can taste and hear. Some words, when spoken, sound like their meanings. They are called onomatopoetic words. Although onomatopoeia is a long tongue- twister, many of the onomatopo- etic words used by ad writers are quite short. Try this list on your ear: *Boom, burst, buzz, chortle, click, crash, fizz, grizzle, growl, hiss, luminous, muck, poof, pop, rock, scratch, shriek, smack, spurt, zip.*

REPEAT AFTER ME

Advertisers rely on repetition. Not only do commercials appear over and over on the radio and TV and in print media, but there is also repeti- tion within ads. Like poets, advertisers repeat particular sounds, groups of sounds, and rhythmic patterns of sound to attract attention and make a lasting impression. One com- mon "trick of the trade" is rhyme. Rhyming sounds usu- ally appear at the ends of words or groups of words: Swiss Miss, Ace is the place, Big Mac Attack. However, both poets and advertisers also use alliteration, as in Peter Pan Peanut Butter, Relaxed Riders, and even throughout words like Coca-Cola, making the brand names easy to remem- ber. Look for these poetic devices in your favourite ads— and poems—today.

WORD TALK

In advertising, **copy** re- fers to the words that accompany a visual im- age. In newspapers, ra- dio, and television, the word *copy* also refers to news or opinion writ- ing that is going to be printed or broadcast.

Another classic device of both ad writers and poets is the simile, a comparison using the words *like* or *as*. "It's like opening a present," promises a Polaroid Color Pack Camera ad, showing a picture of a boy with a half-eaten stick of ice cream. Similes make you see things in a new way.

Ad copy writers know that some words sell products and others don't. They know that *half-full* sounds better than *half-empty,* and that an *engine* sounds more complicated and expensive than a *motor. Thin* is a nicer word than *skinny,* and *artificial* sounds bad for us, but *man-made* sounds good. They know their way around the mysterious world of word-choice, or word-feel, where for no very logical reason certain words make us feel stingy or cheap, while other words make us feel flush and fine and ready to part with our hard-earned money. Ad copy writers say that even particular syllables convey feelings. For example, they suggest that words containing the syllable "eep" convey low or mean feelings, words containing "eal" are weak and unhealthy, and words with "urk" are evil, grotesque, or abnormal.

Advertisers know that poetry in any language can move people. David Chan and David Chow design ads for a growing Chinese market in Toronto.

But are ad writers really poets? Aren't they just selling a product or a company? Laundry detergent, jeans, hair spray, or sneakers—it's all the same to them. True poets have something more serious to say. Right?

Well, that's partly right. But the best ad writers know that they are selling more than a product. They're aware that aside from variations in packaging, most products are surprisingly similar. There's not much difference among fluoride toothpastes, or between one dog bis-cuit and another. If you took the labels off all the jeans in a clothing store, could you tell the brands apart? Ad writers must distinguish their product in some way to set it off from the pack. So, like poets, they try to sell us a mood or a sunset, a feeling or a point of view. They must wake us up, surprise us, shock us, or give us a happy ending.

An ad must persuade you that it's not just dog biscuits in that box. It's your dog's love and affection. It's not just a pair of jeans attached to that label. It's romance, glamour, popularity. The right toothpaste will brighten not just teeth but your whole morning, help solve family arguments, and give you the courage to invite some special person to the high school dance.

Advertising is a big, expensive business. Because the success of a product often rides on the words an advertising copy writer strings together, every word must sell. In 1992, Canada spent more than ten billion dollars on advertising, almost all of it to pay for media space. With that much money on the line, no advertising copy can afford to laze around. Every word must literally be worth its weight in gold.

EXPRESS YOURSELF

Design an advertisement for a product you like. Try using some of the techniques suggested in this article to communicate your feelings about it.

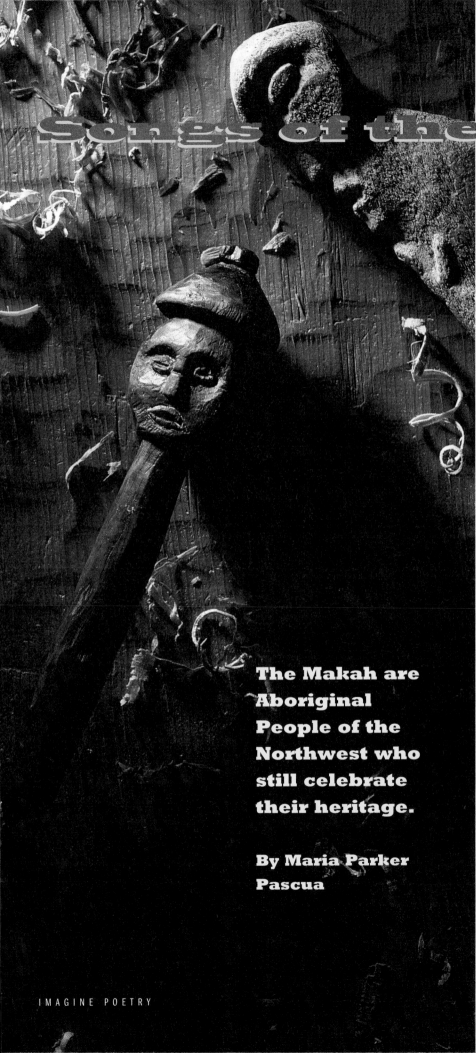

Songs of the Makah

The Makah are Aboriginal People of the Northwest who still celebrate their heritage.

By Maria Parker Pascua

What does the author learn about how important language was to her ancestors?

In January of 1970, Pacific storms uncovered one of many centuries-old Makah beach settlements near the border of Canada and the United States. The village of Ozette, buried in a mudslide around A.D. 1500, underwent a ten-year archaeological excavation. Aided by testimonies and oral history gathered from descendants, the dig helped complete a picture of the pre-Columbian Makah who were whalers. The following essay journeys back in time to describe the importance of song in tribal life.

More valuable than a family's material possessions are its songs. Most songs are received in visions or dreams. Their verses are brief, woven in and out of a chanting melody as a box drum keeps beat.

Songs are a privilege and must be cared for, honoured, and properly sung and danced. Their origin and history must be learned, repeated, and passed down to each generation.

The Makah carved most of their tools from wood, such as the handle of this beaver-tooth knife.

Preserving the Language

Today there are fewer than twenty people who speak the Makah language fluently, because the United States government discouraged use of native languages during the nineteenth century. Now there is a movement to restore the Makah language before it disappears altogether. The Makah Cultural and Research Center in Neah Bay in the state of Washington has formed a program funded by the U.S. government to teach the language in local schools.

First, language researchers recorded conversations among the Makah elders who still used the laguage. Then they developed an alphabet of the language's sounds. As they teach this alphabet to young people and their parents, they hope to develop a way to preserve the Makah traditions and history.

A song can be sung only by its owners, though others may be asked to learn a song to help perform it. If the owner of a song dies before passing it down at a potlatch, the song dies also, unless permission was given for someone to carry it on.

There are songs of joy, of war, and of love:

No matter how hard I try to
    forget you,
you always come back to my mind,
and when you hear me singing you
    may know
I am weeping for you.

RECORDED BY YOUNG DOCTOR,
1851–1934

When a chief hosts a potlatch, families are invited to dance their songs and to display the ceremonial dress and masks they usually keep hidden. Important occasions call for a potlatch—a wedding, a daughter's coming of age, the end of a year of mourning.

But the primary purpose is to validate a Makah chief's ownership of his family songs, his ceremonial names, the crests that decorate his robes and possessions. To repay his guests for witnessing and validating his claims,

WORD TALK

A **potlatch** is a ceremony at which the host gives the guests many of his possessions in a show of wealth and generosity. The less the host is left with, the more successful the potlatch. Each potlatch is more elaborate than the previous one, and thus the host of one will never be too long without material possessions.

the host will give away virtually everything he owns.

Messengers fan out in canoes to invite families from the other Makah villages and from neighbouring villages where other languages are spoken. Several interpreters are needed.

How much a chief is able to give away will affect his standing. His guests will be fed the best food, given the finest blankets and the most handsome boxes. The chief knows that his gifts will be reciprocated with interest at future potlatches.

The families are called by rank to perform their songs. This is their great gift to the host, to which they add presents for his family and fellow guests.

If a family is in mourning and therefore unable to sing and dance, it will ask another family if it can "ride in their canoe." In this way the mourning family can be spiritually present in the other family's song. Then, finally, the host's family performs its songs.

A Makah elder cradles a 500-year-old, carved wood figure in a mussel shell.

Songs are a privilege. . . . Their origin and history must be learned, repeated, and passed down to each generation.

The Makah elders alive in 1991 remember potlatches that went for two weeks without a song being repeated. Today a potlatch lasts but a night. We have no way of knowing how many songs were lost in the epidemics, how many were lost through the persistent efforts of missionaries and federal Indian agents to suppress our language and culture.

MARIA PARKER PASCUA *has dedicated her life to passing on the traditions of the Makah people. She is currently a teacher at her local elementary school.*

EXPRESS
YOURSELF

Think about songs that are most familiar and most important to you. Why are they important? Choose a favourite song, and tell in what sense that song "belongs" to you.

Killer whales and human faces were carved on a rock on the Northwest coast centuries ago.

changes

Yellow is . . .

The dazzling sun that ripens the sweet summer corn.
An amber ring that shimmers on my finger.
Golden dandelions that sway in the gentle spring
    breeze.
The rich custard pie that drips sinfully down my
    cheek.
The luscious sulphur lemon that will soon be
    lemonade.

LISA BULLOCK

LISA BULLOCK *wrote this poem when she was in grade nine in British Columbia. She has been writing poetry since she was in grade four.*

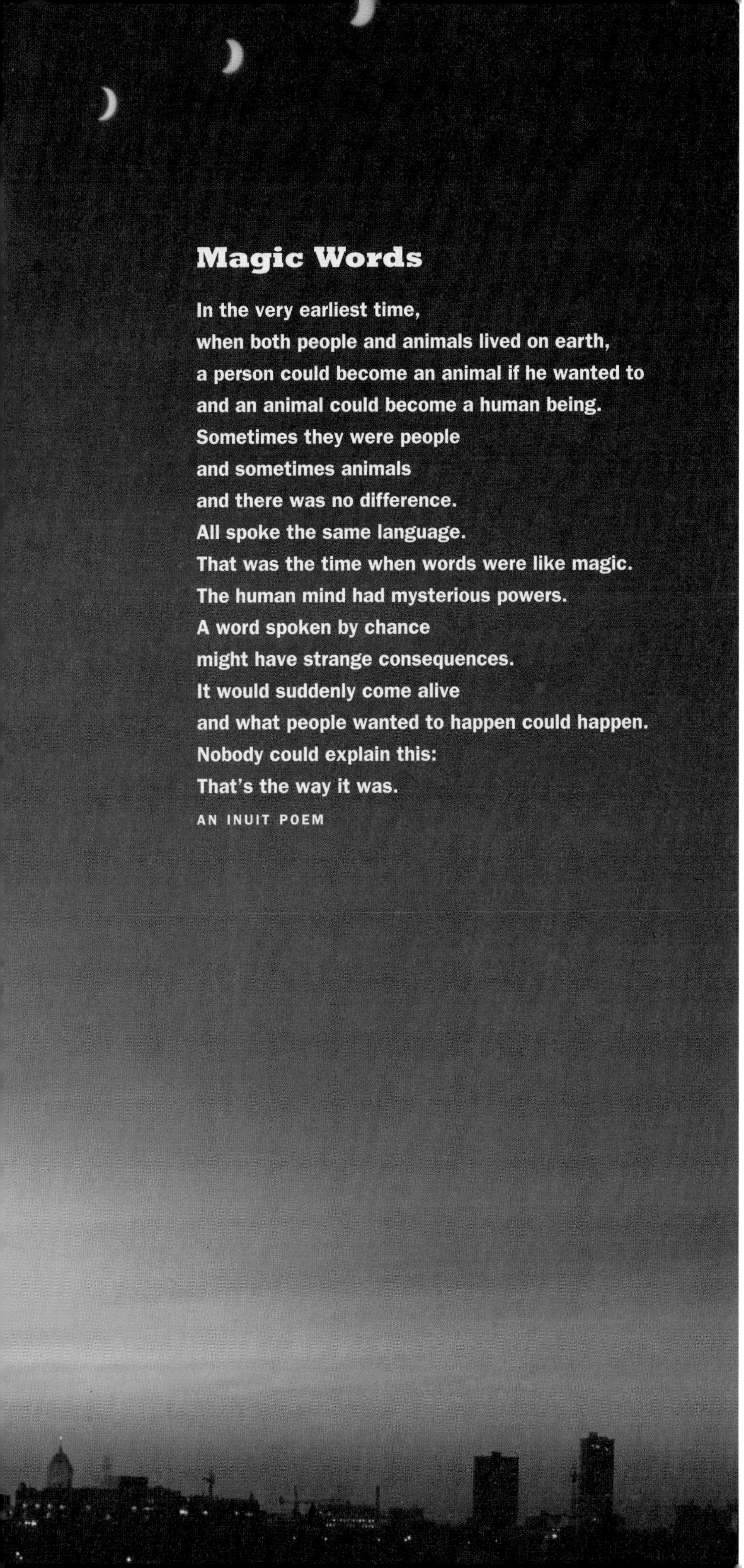

Magic Words

In the very earliest time,
when both people and animals lived on earth,
a person could become an animal if he wanted to
and an animal could become a human being.
Sometimes they were people
and sometimes animals
and there was no difference.
All spoke the same language.
That was the time when words were like magic.
The human mind had mysterious powers.
A word spoken by chance
might have strange consequences.
It would suddenly come alive
and what people wanted to happen could happen.
Nobody could explain this:
That's the way it was.

AN INUIT POEM

Four Dancers

the winds
are four dancers
that become
many dances

they rise
in the distance
in a place
that is stillness

they hear
a heart beat
and dance
its rhythms

they dance
in the distance
and dance
in our presence

they dance
in our words
they dance
in our breathing

they dance
our world
they dance
our being

the winds
are four dancers
that become
many dances

JIM TALLOSI

JIM TALLOSI *was
born in Hungary in
1947 and later moved
to Manitoba. He pub-
lished his first book of
poetry in 1981.*

The phases of a solar eclipse above the
skyline of Winnipeg, Manitoba

The Distant Drum

I am not a metaphor or symbol.

This you hear is not the wind in the trees,

Nor a cat being maimed in the street.

I am being maimed in the street.

It is I who weep, laugh, feel pain or joy.

Speak this because I exist.

This is my voice.

These words are my words,

My mouth speaks them,

My hand writes—

I am a poet.

It is my fist you hear

Beating against your ear.

CALVIN C. HERNTON

CALVIN C. HERNTON *is a fiction writer and poetry editor living in New York. He has also written plays, some of which were produced at the colleges where he taught English.*

Why do dictators fear poets?

ANNA AKHMATOVA:

Did you know that writing poetry can be dangerous? "Impossible!" you might object, but today, in places such as South Africa and Central America, for a few lines of poetry heroic men and women are suffering imprisonment, terrible beatings, torture, and even death. Poems can inspire ordinary people to act courageously—even to challenge their rulers—and thus poems can frighten and enrage the powerful. Poems—and poets—can have enormous force.

Anna Akhmatova was a poet of enormous force. Born in Russia in 1889, she survived the horrors of the Russian Revolution, two world wars, and what we refer to today as the "terror"—the mass killings of millions of Russians by Joseph Stalin, who until his death in 1953 was the brutal leader of the Soviet Union. During those tragic times some Russians committed suicide. Many fled.

Akhmatova remained. "I am not one of those who left the land," she wrote in 1922 in a poem about the

ONE SMALL VOICE

By Laura Ricard

Russians who had exiled themselves:

> *But I pity the exile's lot.*
> *Like a felon, like a man half-dead,*
> *dark is your path, wanderer;*
> *wormwood infects your foreign bread . . .*
> *We are the people without tears,*
> *straighter than you . . . more proud. . . .*

Akhmatova chose to stay with her people and suffer with them through a "cruel age." By staying behind she became a witness to the horrors of that period, but she also gave voice to the suffering of her people.

When she was a young woman, Anna Akhmatova's poems made her famous. Her work was read throughout Russia. She was adored and imitated, and critics compared her to Sappho, a great poet of ancient Greece. But World War I broke out in 1914, and then in 1917 civil war ripped her country apart. The victorious Communist party soon issued an order that none of Akhmatova's poems could be published. From that point on, the Soviet government persecuted Akhmatova for most of her life.

Why? Why would a powerful government bother with a solitary poet? Because Akhmatova's pen was as powerful—maybe even more powerful—than the sword of government.

Akhmatova wrote from personal experience. Falsely accused of conspiracy, her first husband was shot. Her only son spent years in prison. Her third husband was arrested—"At dawn they came and took you away," she wrote of him—and he died in prison. Without government support, Akhmatova lived in poverty. She suffered the ravages of sickness, fear, humiliation, and hunger.

In spite of her suffering—or perhaps because of it—Akhmatova was able to capture in her poems the very essence of what war, fear, imprisonment, and murder had done to the Russian people. Akhmatova had spiritual strength. Dictators recognize this quality immediately and fear it. They try to destroy it because it is something they cannot control. Akhmatova was a threat to Stalin because through her poetry she shared with others the strength and courage they needed to resist him—if only in their hearts.

So Stalin tried to crush her, but Akhmatova survived. Try as he might, he could not overcome her.

Curiously, for people of a passionate nature, stressful experiences often lead to creativity. This proved to be so for Akhmatova, whose whole life bore witness to her belief that a poet must speak out against cruelty and injustice. Her finest poems, all of which we may read today, grew out of her darkest moments. In winter's cold and summer's heat, with thousands of other women—mothers, wives, sisters—Akhmatova waited outside Leningrad's infamous Kresty Prison for word of her beloved son. The anguish she suffered waiting outside the "blind red wall" of the prison and expressed in her poem "Requiem" communicated the anguish of her people.

LAURA RICARD, *born in 1949, is a writer and teacher with a history degree. She is in the process of publishing her first book about living in an isolated New Brunswick farmhouse with her husband and daughter.*

REQUIEM

No foreign sky protected me,
no stranger's wing shielded my face.
I stand as witness to the common lot,
survivor of that time, that place.

ANNA AKHMATOVA, 1961

EXPRESS
YOURSELF

Although she knew it could be dangerous, Anna Akhmatova decided to stay in Russia after many of her friends had left. Did the poet gain anything by staying behind? What do you think you would have done in her position? Why?

double

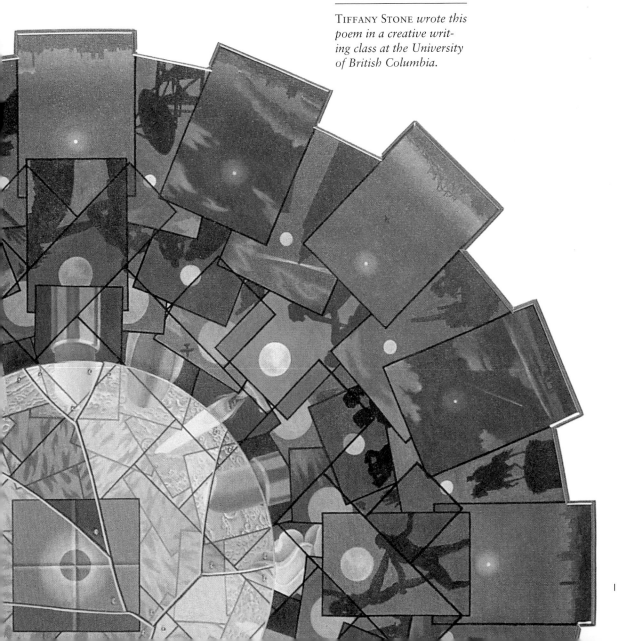

rush hour in
the rain

What can a poet see by taking a second look?

wet streets

shiny black like licorice

twisting through the city

traffic tastes its way home

TIFFANY STONE

TIFFANY STONE *wrote this poem in a creative writing class at the University of British Columbia.*

take!

Jetliner

now he takes his mark
at the very farthest end of the runway
looking straight ahead, eager, intense
with his sharp eyes shining

he takes a deep, deep breath
with his powerful lungs
expanding his massive chest
his burning heart beating like thunders

then . . . after a few . . . tense moments . . . of pondering
he roars at his utmost
and slowly begins to jog
kicking the dark earth hard
and now he begins to run
kicking the dark earth harder
then he dashes, dashes like mad, like mad
howling, shouting, screaming, and roaring

then with a most violent kick
he shakes off the earth's pull
softly lifting himself into the air
soaring higher and higher and higher still
piercing the sea of clouds
up into the chandelier of stars

NAOSHI KORIYAMA

NAOSHI KORIYAMA *is an English professor at Toyo University in Japan. He writes poetry in English even though his native language is Japanese. He has published six books of poetry.*

Zebra

white sun	morning
black	grazing like a zebra
fire escape,	outside my window.

JUDITH THURMAN

JUDITH THURMAN *was born in New York in 1946 and grew up in the city. She writes poetry and books about poets, besides working as an interpreter and reading teacher.*

EXPRESS
YOURSELF

Take a close look at something familiar, such as a desk lamp, a tree, or a ballpoint pen. Then imagine that you are seeing the object for the first time, or that you are seeing it from another person's point of view. By looking at it in a new way, what can you see?

Computer Poetry

Computers are being programmed to write poetry.

Throughout history, poets have been thought of as exceptional individuals. Some were believed to have an unusual understanding of the natural world—or even control over it. Others were given positions of power in the royal courts and paid handsomely to write poetry for their king or queen. Although today's poets are not often held in quite such high esteem, most people would agree that poets possess "something special"— something not found in other people and certainly not found in machines!

Computers are no longer the mere number crunchers they were in the fifties. Computers in the 1990s can talk, fly airplanes, play chess, and give advice. But can they write poetry? Some people believe they can.

A computer program named *P1.0*, invented by Raymond Kurzweil, can "read" poetry written by a human poet and then produce a "poem" modelled on the original. This poem by *P1.0* was "inspired" by William Carlos Williams' poetry.

> we loved
> the delicate
> imperfect foam, yellow weed
> strands, stems, debris—
> firmament

Now compare *P1.0*'s version to the following poem written by William Carlos Williams. Can you recognize the "human element" that makes these two poems different?

The Red Wheelbarrow

so much depends
upon

a red wheel
barrow

glazed with rain
water

beside the white
chickens.

Another smart machine, called the Computer Poet, is stationed at card and gift shops. Developed by a computer programmer and a poet, the Computer Poet composes personalized limericks. You answer a series of questions about the person to whom you want to send a greeting card, and the Computer Poet produces a tailor-made limerick. Just attach the printed message to a blank greeting card, and send off your personal poem!

Does the fact that computers can perform these limited tasks mean that they really possess intelligence? Do they have that special something that will allow them to become the poets of the future? We shall have to wait and see.

Poetry in Motion

A poem can celebrate a moment of athletic achievement.

Then out, onto the ice, blades
dividing
the surface into geometry,
ice writing from an old language,
the calligraphy of snow. . . .

from "Skating after School"
by Barbara Crooker

Although poetry is an ancient art form, there will always be new poems to write: perhaps a new way of seeing, feeling, or experiencing something that may seem familiar. We must pay careful attention to the wonder in our lives so we don't miss the magical in the everyday.

For example, everyone can appreciate the common feelings that spring from engaging in physical activity. The majority of us will never hear the roar of fans cheering our name, will never receive the blue ribbon or gold medal or winner's trophy. Nevertheless, as we celebrate the victories and mourn the defeats in our own lives, we can appreciate the deeper understanding they bring us.

We can all imagine the glow of the victorious athlete, the throbbing

Kristi Yamaguchi, 1992
Winter Olympics gold
medal winner.

pain of sore muscles, the frustration of a missed play, the joy of being part of a team, the isolation of being left out of the contest. It is this humanity, whether played out in sports or in some other arena, that we can celebrate in poetry.

Activities

FIND out more about a favourite poet. What kind of poetry did "your" poet write? What concerns and interests were important to that poet? How did events in the poet's life affect his or her writing? What poetic techniques did the poet use? Present a report to the class. Choose several poems to include in your report.

IMAGINE what the world would be like if poetry disappeared. If you got out of bed tomorrow and poetry no longer existed, what would be missing? Make a list of the various items that would no longer be part of your day. Begin your list with the morning and go through a typical day. What would you no longer see or hear or do? What difference would it make if poetry were missing?

INTERVIEW your parents or an older person about the songs that are most important to them. Ask them to explain why the songs are important. How often do they listen to those songs? What were their favourite songs when they were your age? What can a person's favourite songs show about that person? What do they show about the person you interviewed?

CREATE a group poem with your classmates. Gather in small groups of three or four students. Decide on a subject for your poem, and decide what feelings you want the poem to communicate. Write a beginning for the poem, and take turns adding words and lines until the poem seems complete. What is gained by working on a poem together? What is lost? Is the subject matter different for a group poem? Why?

Co-operative Activity

PRODUCING A BOOK **Working together as a class, create a book of poetry.** Decide what should be included in the book. Suggestions might be student poems, music, articles about individual poets, illustrations of poems, and photo essays. Gather in small groups to plan and create each section of the book. Write a title and design a cover. Then share your book with another class. Find out how you might get your book printed.

REREAD **"Greatness" by Alden Nowlan on page 17.** Then read "Sound of Water" by Mary O'Neill and "The Skaters" by John Gould Fletcher in the *Imagine Poetry Anthology*. Notice how these poems use a few words to create an image in your mind. Now pick something to describe and create a word picture of your own, using a few carefully chosen words.

Exploring Further

For more information about the Makah and other Aboriginal Peoples, read the October 1991 issue of **National Geographic,** from which the article in this magazine is taken.

If you like vocal music, you will enjoy listening to **Cats,** the musical composed by **Andrew Lloyd Webber.** It is available in many recordings. Cat lovers should read **Old Possum's Book of Practical Cats,** the book of poems by **T. S. Eliot** that inspired the musical.

For more about Anna Akhmatova, read **Poems of Akhmatova,** edited and translated by **Stanley Kunitz.**

If you enjoy limericks, there are many collections to choose from. The following books will tickle your funny bone: **A Lolligag of Limericks** by **Myra Cohn Livingston; They've Discovered a Head in the Box for the Bread, and Other Laughable Limericks** collected by **John Brewton** and **Lorraine Blackburn;** or **Wizz!** by **Edward Lear.**

For information about rap and rap artists, read the book **Rap** by **Keith Elliot Greenberg.**

Roald Dahl wrote many fractured fairy tales, parodies, and nonsense rhymes. You can find them in his books **Revolting Rhymes** and **Rhyme Stew.**

If you would like to try getting your own poetry published, you can send it to one of the following magazines. Your school or library may have a complete list of publications.

Windscript
Saskatchewan Writer's Guild
2049 Lorne Street
Regina, Saskatchewan S4P 2M4

The Monitor
(grades 6–8)
30 St. Clair Avenue West
Toronto, Ontario M4V 3A1

Chiboo's Corner
(ages 7–15)
P.O. Box 745
Sydney, Nova Scotia B1P 6H7

Credits

A Ligature Book

Photos

Cover © Jerry Lofaro/The Image Bank; **1** © Deborah Samuel/ Visages (tl); Courtesy of Lisa Bullock (br); © Natalie Fobes (tr); © Harvey Studios/Courtesy of Claudine Nowlan (cl); **2** Anne Ghory-Goodman (l); Courtesy of the Phyllis Kind Galleries, Chicago and New York (tr); **3** Ivan Chermayeff; **4** © Ron Rovtar/Photonica (l); **4–5** © John Kelly/The Image Bank; **6** © 1986 Martha Swope; **7** Giraudon/Art Resource, NY; **16** Haags Gemeentemusem; **18** © Deborah Samuel/Visages (l); **18–19** © Peter Ashworth; **20** © Deborah Samuel/Visages (both); **24-25** Photo by Laura Chapman/Sculpture by Patricia Rennick; **25** Ivan Chermayeff (tr); **26** Columbus Museum of Art, Ohio: Gift of Mary Nancy Davis; **27** Ivan Chermayeff (tr); **30** © Myrleen Ferguson/Photo Edit; **32** Photo by Viliam; **33–35** © Lynn Johnson/ Black Star; **36–37** Henry Groskinsky, *Life* magazine © 1979 Time Warner, Inc.; **38** Anne Ghory-Goodman; **39** Karl Model (r); © Sovfoto (l); **40-41** © Don Carroll/The Image Bank; **42** Courtesy of The Phyllis Kind Galleries, Chicago and New York; **43** © Jonnie Miles/ Photonica; **45** © David Madison/duomo

Text

Grateful acknowledgment is given to authors, publishers, and agents for permission to reprint the following copyrighted material. Every effort has been made to determine copyright owners. In the case of any omissions, the Publisher will be pleased to make suitable acknowledgments in future editions.

4 "You are reading this too fast...", excerpt of a poem by Ken Norris from *Whirlwinds*, copyright © 1983 by Ken Norris Published by Guernica Editions.

6 "The Ad-dressing of Cats" by T.S. Eliot from *Old Possums' Book of Practical Cats*, by T.S. Eliot. Copyright © 1967 by Esme Valerie Eliot. Published by Faber & Faber Limited.

7 "Around the eyes" by George Swede from *Do Whales Jump at Night?* edited by Florence McNeil. Copyright © 1990 by Douglas & McIntryre Ltd. Reprinted by permission of the author.

8 "How To Eat a Poem" by Eve Merriam from *A Sky Full of Poems* by Eve Merriam. Copyright © 1964, 1970, 1973 by Eve Merriam. Reprinted by permission of Marion Reiner, Permissions Consultant.

10 "What Can a Poem Do?" by Eve Merriam appeared in *The Writer*, April 1991. Copyright © 1989 by Eve Merriam. Reprinted by permission of Marion Reiner, Permissions Consultant.

17 "I Want To Write" by Margaret Walker from *October Journey*. Copyright © 1973 by Margaret Walker. Reprinted by permission of the author and Broadside Press; "Greatness" by Alden Nowlan from *An Exchange of Gifts* by Alden Nowlan. Copyright © 1985 by Irwin Publishing Inc. Used by permission of Stoddart Publishing Co. Limited, 34 Lesmill Road, Don Mills, Ontario; "My Poems" by Robert Currie used by permission of the author; "A Seeing Poem" by Robert Froman. Copyright © 1974 by Robert Froman.

22 From ROALD DAHL'S REVOLTING RHYMES by Roald Dahl. Text copyright © 1982 by Roald Dahl. Reprinted by permission of Alfred A. Knopf, Inc.

24 "Valentine for Ernest Mann" by Naomi Shihab Nye appeared in *Green Rain: An Anthology for Teachers* published by the San Antonio Independent School District. Reprinted by permission of the author.

27 Comment on "The Rider" by Naomi Shihab Nye appeared in *Poetspeak: In their work, about their work* edited by Paul B. Janeczko. Published by Bradbury Press, an affiliate of Macmillan, Inc. Copyright © 1990 by Naomi Shihab Nye. Reprinted by permission of Naomi Shihab Nye.

29 "l(a" is reprinted from COMPLETE POEMS, 1904–1062, by e.e. cummings, edited by George J. Firmage, by permission of Liveright Publishing Corporation. Copyright © 1923, 1925, 1926, 1931, 1935, 1938, 1939, 1940, 1944, 1945, 1946, 1947, 1948, 1949, 1950, 1951, 1952, 1953, 1954, 1955, 1956, 1957, 1958, 1959, 1960, 1961, 1962 by e.e. cummings. Copyright © 1961, 1963, 1966, 1967, 1968 by Marion Morehouse Cummings. Copyright © 1972, 1973, 1974, 1975, 1976, 1977, 1978, 1979, 1980, 1981, 1982, 1983, 1984, 1985, 1986, 1987, 1988, 1989, 1990, 1991 by the Trustees for the E.E. Cummings Trust.

33 "Ozette: A Makah Village in 1491" by Maria Parker Pascua appeared in *National Geographic Magazine*, Volume 180, Number 4, October 1991.

36 "Yellow is..." by Lisa Bullock appeared in the *British Columbia English Teachers' Association Student Writing Journal*, 1991–1992. Used by permission of the author.

37 "Magic Words" from *Songs and Stories of the Netsilik Eskimos* translated by Edward Fields from text collected by Knud Rasmussen. Courtesy of Education Development Center, Inc. Newton, MA and the heirs of Knud Rasmussen.; "Four Dancers" by Jim Tallosi appeared in *Native Writers and Canadian Writing* edited by W. H. New, University of British Columbia Press.

38 "Distant Drum" by Calvin C. Hernton appeared in *New Negro Poets U.S.A.* edited by Langston Hughes. Copyright © 1964 by Langston Hughes. Published by Indiana University Press.

41 "Requiem 1935–1940" by Anna Akhmatova from *Poems of Akhmatova* selected, translated, and introduced by Stanley Kunitz with Max Hayward. Copyright © 1973 by Stanley Kunitz and Max Hayward. Originally published in THE ATLANTIC. By permission of Little, Brown & Co.

42 "rush hour in the rain" by Tiffany Stone from *Do Whales Jump at Night?* edited by Florence McNeil. Published by Douglas & McIntyre Ltd. Reprinted by permission of Tiffany Stone.

43 "Jetliner" by Naoshi Koriyama is reprinted from *Poetry Nippon (Summer 1970)* by permission of the author. Copyright © 1970 by The Poetry Society of Japan, Nagoya, Japan; "Zebra" by Judith Thurman from FLASHLIGHT AND OTHER POEMS by Judith Thurman. Copyright © 1976 by Judith Thurman. Copyright © 1976 by Judith Thurman. Reprinted by permission of Marian Reiner, Permissions Consultant for the author.

44 "The Red Wheelbarrow" by William Carlos Williams: The Collected Poems of William Carlos Williams, 1909–1939, vol. I. Copyright 1938 by New Directions Publishing Corporation.

45 "Skating After School" by Barbara Crooker. Reprinted by permission of the author.

Canadian Cataloguing in Publication Data

Main entry under title:

Imagine Poetry : magazine

(MultiSource)

ISBN 0-13-017963-9

1. Children's poetry. 2. Poetics—Juvenile literature. I. Iveson, Margaret L., 1948– II. Robinson, Sam 1937– . III. Series

PZ8.3.I554 1993   j808.81   C92–095225–9